Sedum Spurium

Wildcats

Alicante, Spain

Butterfly on finger

Sunset

£1.55

Printed and published in Great Britian by D. C. THOMSON & CO., LTD., 185 Fleet Street, London EC4A 2HS.
© D. C. THOMSON & CO., LTD., 1981.
ISBN 0 85116 205 3

LOST SATURDAY

IT was the first Saturday of the summer holidays and Carla Trent was lost. She had intended to pay a surprise visit to her friend, Sandra, but could not find the address. Fortunately, a passing motorist came to her rescue when she explained what had happened.

So is there a 'phone-box here, please?

But you're soaking! Get in . . . you can 'phone from my house.

A little later—

Oh! It's snowing!

There's no knowing with our weather, is there? I expect my daughter will know your friend. She's about your age.

Soon—

We're the first people to move on to this new development. My daughter's having a housewarming party tonight.

She still doesn't seem to be surprised at the snow . . . in August! I've heard of hailstones in summer, but snow is surely rare!

Inside—

Yes, I know Sandra Baker—but Lisa hasn't met her yet. Shall I give Sandra a ring and ask her over?

Yes, please, Roy. Come in, Carla, and join the party.

Here, try these—made them myself!

Sandra's on her way over.

Thanks, Lisa . . . thanks, Roy! This is a great party!

But after an hour passed—

I don't understand it! Sandra should have been here by now! And all this snow in the middle of summer!

I'll take a look outside to see if she's coming. Ah! There's a car. She could be in it.

No, that's not her . . . Oh! It's going to skid into that hole! There'll be an explosion! The house . . . !

Aaaah!

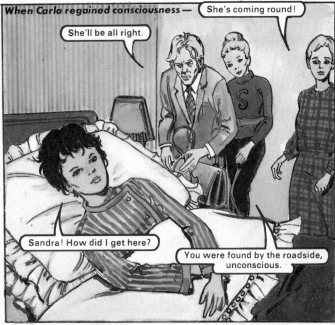

When Carla regained consciousness—

She's coming round!

She'll be all right.

Sandra! How did I get here?

You were found by the roadside, unconscious.

Oh! There was an accident . . . and explosion! A car skidded in the snow! All the people in that house . . .

Snow, in August? You must have been dreaming.

And those houses where you were found are all empty! Not one of them is even finished yet!

Later that day, Carla's father came to fetch her.

Thanks for everything, Sandra. If you find my handbag—let me know.

Right! And next time you're coming, give me a ring, OK?

As the months passed, the memory of Carla's strange experience faded.

Look, Mum! That's just what I'll get Sandra for Christmas!

Then the week before Christmas—

Yes, Sandra, I'd love to go to a party with you.

It's some new people who've moved into town. See you Saturday, then.

So the following Saturday —

Wait a minute! This is—I'm sure it is! It's the place I . . . I . . . had that dream about in the summer! I've been here before!

Don't be daft! They didn't finish building it till last month!

GAS BOARD BEWARE NO NAKED LIGHTS

Sandra told me all about you, Carla. I'm Lisa, and this is Roy.

But . . . but . . . haven't we met before?

Not unless you used to live in Dusseldorf! We've only just moved back here from Germany. Come and get some food.

A few minutes later—

Hey, whose is this bag? I found it behind the chair.

I—I think it's mine.

But it can't be!

It seems impossible, but it really is my bag—and that must mean that the car out there on the road . . .

Quickly! Everyone outside! Hurry up!

Eh?

It's freezing out there!

8

THE END

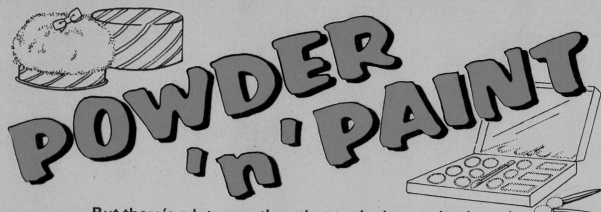

POWDER 'n' PAINT

But there's a lot more than that to the beauty business!
Come with the " Judy " camera into the beauty salon at
Bournes, a big London store . . .

Meet pretty Sofia Gegan, one of the beauticians.

Sofia hands a client some leaflets describing different beauty treatments.

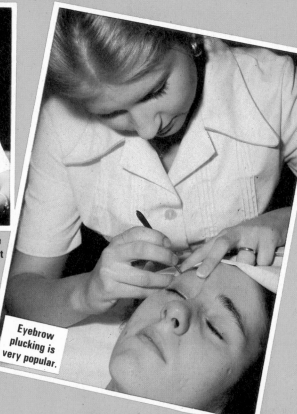

Eyebrow plucking is very popular.

Here, Sofia uses a brush to tint a client's eyelashes.

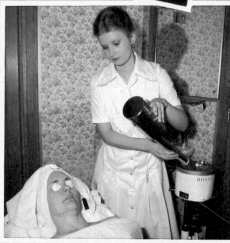

Steam treatment opens the skin pores and helps cleanse away the city grime.

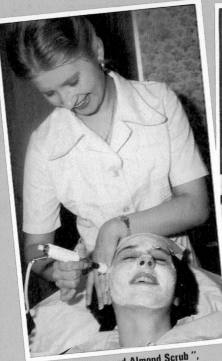

A " Honey and Almond Scrub ", using a soft electric brush, completes the cleansing process.

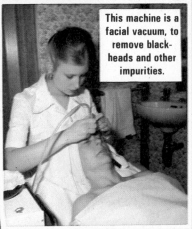

This machine is a facial vacuum, to remove black-heads and other impurities.

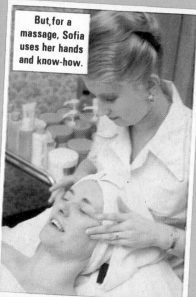

But, for a massage, Sofia uses her hands and know-how.

After applying make-up base, Sofia uses blushers to enhance the shape of the cheek bones.

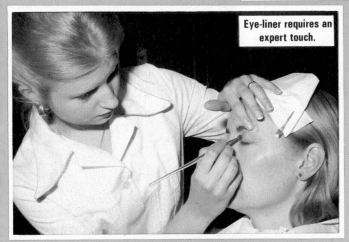

Eye-liner requires an expert touch.

The client admires the final result.

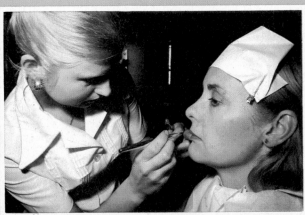

Almost finished now, Sofia applies lipstick.

TURN THE PAGE FOR SOME SUPER TIPS ON DO-IT-YOURSELF BEAUTY TREATMENTS.

Budding Beauty

You're never too young to take an interest in your appearance, so why not make use of items from the kitchen shelves, or growing in the garden, to make some of your own beauty aids?

CUCUMBER:

A good and effective way of giving yourself a quick freshen-up—especially in hot weather—is to use cucumber. The juice is excellent for the skin. Cut off a piece of cucumber, rub it all over the face, then rinse off with cold water. You'll feel marvellous!

LEMONS:

A lemon can serve lots of purposes. For whitening hands that look patchy from a fading sun-tan, cut a lemon in half and rub it onto your skin, while your hands are still wet, every time you wash. Some lemon juice mixed with a little rose water and glycerine makes an excellent hand lotion. And a few drops of lemon juice mixed with a small amount of oatmeal, rubbed well into your elbows and then rinsed off with warm water, will whiten your elbows.

A teaspoonful of lemon juice in the final rinsing water after shampooing will bring out the highlight in fair hair. (Brunettes should use the same quantity of vinegar.)

EGGS:

Here is an excellent treatment for hair, using eggs. Break two eggs into a bowl and lightly beat them. Pour this over your head after shampooing. Leave on for about 10 minutes, before rinsing off with luke-warm water. Rinse thoroughly—but remember to use water that's not too hot. You don't want to end up with scrambled egg on your head!

OATMEAL:

Oatmeal can be useful for cleansing an oily skin. Put a tablespoonful of oatmeal in a little square of muslin. Dip this into warm water and rub it between the hands until it becomes creamy, then massage well into the face. Wash off with cold water.

SALT:

To tone up feet and give relief if they're aching from tight shoes or too much walking, put a handful of salt into water and soak the feet.

For an eye-bath, put one teaspoonful of bicarbonate of soda and one teaspoonful of salt into a pint of boiled water. Mix well, pour into a bottle, and allow to cool. Shake well before using.

JUNIOR NANNY

CHRIS JOHNSON worked in a residential nursery for the under fives. One day a policewoman brought four-year-old Alan to the nursery. Alan, an orphan, had been living with relatives but they had neglected him, so the authorities decided he would be better off away from them.

I'll leave him in your good hands then, Matron. Funny about that bucket. He won't let go of it. You'd think it was the Crown Jewels!

Maybe it is, to him.

Poor child, he's frightened. I don't want to make matters worse by forcing him to part with that bucket. You see what you can do, Nurse Johnson.

Yes, Matron.

Hello, Alan. I'm Nurse Chris. My goodness, that's a lovely bucket!

It's mine! I found it at that place where they put the stuff from the dustbins.

I'm lucky to have Chris on my staff. She has a way with children . . . especially the frightened ones.

That was a very lucky find for you. Would you like to come into the kitchen and have some milk and biscuits?

In the kitchen—

Hey, he's feeding that bucket!

Looks like it! It's obviously more than just a bucket to him, Anne!

Later, when Chris had bathed Alan and given him some clean clothes, she talked to him about his bucket.

He's my friend and his name is Jimmy. But sometimes he's my dog, and then I call him Billy.

That's nice. Do you like toys, Alan?

I dunno. I've never had any.

We've lots in our playroom downstairs. We'll go and look at them, shall we? Then you can play with them, and with the other boys.

13

Alan was delighted with the toys. Chris held his bucket while he climbed on the rocking-horse.

Jimmy wants a ride, too.

The bucket means everything to him, but he'll get used to having toys and friends and then he won't need it.

Chris went to help prepare dinner. A little later—

Quick! Come quick! Alan's knocked Simon down on the floor and he's hitting him ever so hard!

Alan, stop it!

He kicked Jimmy!

I—I didn't kick any Jimmy! I j-just gave that old bucket a little kick!

I should have explained to them about the bucket before I left Alan with them.

Chris explained as best she could, and the children promised not to touch Alan's bucket.

He doesn't trust them, Chris.

He hardly knows them yet. Give him a few days, and he'll be less on the defensive.

A week later, when Chris's boyfriend Andrew came to see her—

Alan's playing on his own again, Chris. Jimmy Bucket is still his only friend.

Maybe he feels a sort of loyalty towards that bucket, because it was a comfort to him when he was having such a bad time of it.

Yes. He plays with the toys, Andrew, but he won't play with the kids.

Quite likely. He's a sensitive kid. Ah, well—it's early days yet.

Two weeks later, Alan and his bucket were still inseparable; it even accompanied him on a shopping trip to town.

Millworth's will be packed with Christmas shoppers, Anne. They aren't going to be amused if they get their ankles clonked with that bucket!

So we'll explain no dogs are allowed in there. Alan will have to tie Billy Bucket to that dog rail.

But Alan wouldn't leave his precious bucket outside and decided it was Jimmy Bucket again.

Ow!

Oh, dear! I'll have to apologise for the umpteenth time! I'll be glad when the kids have finished their Christmas shopping and we can go home.

Next morning, the bucket was Billy again.

Alan, shush! The babies were nicely settled, having their morning nap. Your bucket banging on the stairs has woken them up.

I'm sorry. I'll carry Billy, then, and I'll help you get the babies to sleep again.

He likes the babies, and he's good with them. I wish he got on as well with the older kids, but he's still a loner.

TAKE A TURN ON THE JUDY SKI-COURSE

HERE'S AN EXCITING GAME TO TEST YOUR SKI SKILLS!

Any number can play. Use coloured buttons as counters. Each player must throw a six to start, then use the next throw of the dice to determine the first move.

START HERE

START

ON 1

ON 3

MISS 1 TURN

ON 3

BACK 1

WINNER!

BACK 1

STUCK! BACK 2

MISS 1 TURN

16

As you know, ski-ing is a matter of climbing uphill and speeding down. Why not play the game backwards before you start again?

This girl is brilliant!

A genius! And so young!

Her Finest Hour

HARRIET COLE was the best young pianist of the year at the East London College of Music—but now she hates music and everything connected with it. Why? It all started at 8 p.m. one evening when she gave her first concert . . .

When Harriet finished, the audience and the orchestra gave her a standing ovation.

Encore!

It is a privilege to perform alongside a talent such as yours!

I can hardly believe it! It all went so perfectly!

Newspaper reporters crowded into Harriet's dressing-room.

Miss Cole, when will your next concert be?

My, there's Sir Thomas Bryant . . . the famous conductor!

That was the finest performance of that concerto I have ever heard, Miss Cole.

I . . . I owe music a great deal, Sir Thomas.

The debt is owed by music to you. Goodbye—but I expect to hear much, much more of you in the future.

Dottie's Ye O

pulled it so quickly I couldn't keep my balance. Is Tina OK? I mean, I only sort of grabbed her as I fell—and she did manage to keep hold of her violin, didn't she?

"Oh! Well I'm sure she'll agree to stay on in the orchestra. After all, it *was* an accident, wasn't it? Would you like me to have a word with her? You wouldn't? You don't think it'd help one little bit? Well, OK, then.

HELLO, Miss Spinks, this is Sue . . . Hello! Hello! Are you still there? Oh, good! For a minute I thought you'd gone. Well, I heard the 'phone sort of clatter and . . . Gosh, I'm sorry! I didn't realise I'd made you jump. I suppose you're feeling nervous about the Youth Club play. I can understand that. What? You expect I can? I'm not too sure what you mean, Miss Spinks.

"Oh! Oh, I see! Yes, I'm really sorry about that . . . mm. Honest, I didn't know I was standing on the hem of the curtain. Well, Molly Hardacre

"After all, it *was* only a dress rehearsal, wasn't it? That's what *you* thought so why did I turn up dressed in jeans when I'm supposed to be a kitchen maid? It's just that I wanted to add a bit of atmosphere to the part.

"I'm only on stage for a few minutes, aren't I? I thought I could make the part more *interesting.* I mean, people would notice the kitchen maid more if she looked sort of with-it and up-to-date, wouldn't they? Well, yes, I know it's supposed to be a Victorian melodrama, but . . .

22

SEZ SUE

"What have I done with the little white cap and apron the wardrobe department gave me? Well, actually, that's kind of really the point. I was practising at home, see? I sort of got carried away and when I was taking the tray of tea into the front room I sort of slipped.

"The apron and cap are in the washing machine at the moment . . . mm. Mum wasn't too pleased, either. She can't get the stain out of the carpet.

"You know how she feels? Good. Anyway, I've got my lines right now . . . word perfect. You hope so, because if you hear the sentence 'Tea, Lady Kee?' read as "Kee, Lady Tea?' one more time you'll go bananas?

"That's good, because actually what I was ringing to say was that I'd heard Linda Collins has gone down with 'flu and the thing is—I wondered if I could take over her part. I mean, it's the biggest one, and she's on stage all the time, and I'm sure I could handle it, and . . Miss Spinks, are you there? Miss Spinks . . . ?"

DANGER, MIN AT WORK!

EVER since she had left school, Min's hardest job had been keeping a job. Now that she really needed work she had found some—kneading bread in a bakery. Anything to earn a crust!

This is a gluey job, but I've got to stick it out.

Min, you've got the sack.

The sack? Oh, no, not already!

Yes, you've got the sack caught on your foot!

Oh! The flour sack! Oooh! Thank goodness for that!

Later—

Knock the loaves out, then stack up the tins.

Right!

CLANK!

Not that high!

Too late!

CLONK!

OOF!

You'll have to get the bread out on your own. I'll have to have my head seen to . . .

Not for the bump, but for letting her work here!

Tra-laaa! This is great fun!

But—

Ooops! Now what have I done?

CLUNK!

SLURK!

24

25

CRACKER CROSSWORD

Clues Across

1. ' Deep and — and even.' (5)
3. Short for ' Christmas.' (4)
6. John may get a—man outfit (5)
15. It may hum as it spins. (3)
17. ' — in a manger.' (4)
18. A long name for the birth of Jesus. (8)
19. Santa's steed. (8)
20. The Ark was full of them (7)
21. An idea (7)
24. They — no room in the Inn. (3)
25. You may get a pink — mouse in your stocking. (5)
26. Name for the Christmas log. (4)
27. You may see Rod and his — on TV. (3)
28. Over there. (3)

Clues Down

1. Many are sent at Christmas-time. (5)
2. Mother uses — sugar for the cake. (5)
4. ' We wish you a — Christmas.' (5)
5. Jesus lay in a manger —. (5)
6. Tom will — his top. (4)
7. A clock which awakes you early in the morning. (5)
8. The Wise Men came from the—(4)
9. A Christmas song. (5)
10. A small measurement. (4)
11. ' Silent —, holy —. (5)
12. A stormy Christmas Day could be— (5)
13. Mummy's tights are made of this. (5)
14. You may get a — or pencil set. (3)
16. — Christmas Day in the morning.' (2)
22. — to bed on Christmas Eve. (2)
23. You may be going — the Pantomime. (2)

ANSWERS AT THE FOOT OF THE PAGE

THE *LATEST* THING! PUT ONE OF THESE, FILLED WITH SWEETS, BESIDE EACH GUEST'S PLACE AT YOUR CHRISTMAS-PARTY. LOTS OF OTHER USES, TOO!

ADD TAB

FIRST, MAKE THE TWO SHAPES AS DETAILED *HERE* → THEN TRACE ROUND THE SMALLER ONE, ON THIN CARD, FOUR TIMES SIDE BY SIDE, AS ABOVE. BEND ROUND AND GLUE THE TAB AS AT 'A'!

YOU SEE TWO PATTERN SHAPES HERE, SUPERIMPOSED ON EACH OTHER TO SAVE SPACE.

TRACE ROUND EACH ONE CAREFULLY, THEN CUT OUT IN STOUT CARDBOARD.

PARTY BOX MAKER

THEN, FOLD THE TWO FLAPS AS IN 'B' ABOVE, ANOTHER LIKE *THIS* ...

... AND THE LAST ONE LIKE *THIS* ...

... *FINISHING* AS ABOVE, INSIDE IT LOOKS LIKE *THIS*. THIS IS THE LID.

MAKE THE BOTTOM SECTION THE SAME WAY, BUT USING THE LARGER SHAPE.

CLEVER OLD *YOU!*

DECORATE YOUR BOXES BY COVERING WITH PRETTY PAPER, OR PAINTING WITH POSTER COLOURS.

Answers:

Across:—1. Crisp 3. Xmas 6. Space 15. Top 17. Away 18. Nativity 19. Reindeer. 20. Animals 21. Thought 24. Had 25. Sugar 26. Yule 27. Emu 28. Yon. Down:—1. Cards 2. Icing 4. Merry 5. Stall 6. Spin 7. Alarm 8. East 9. Carol 10. Inch 11. Night 12. Windy 13. Nylon 14. Pen 16. On 22. Go 23. To.

31

THE MEAT·PIE PONY

THE ten-month-old foal stood in the disused pigsty, huddled and unhappy. We hadn't meant to buy a pony—only a rabbit. Instead, we bought the miserable little piebald colt who, the man said, was being fattened for the horsemeat trade.

We called him Prince and he became lawnmower-in-chief to keep our small paddock and back garden tidy.

While we waited nearly three years for him to grow up and reach his eventual eleven hands height, we spent pounds on his welfare.

A growing pony eats his head off and cannot repay his owner until he is at least three years old and has been broken-in and schooled to accept a rider on his back. Even then, it is unwise to put the pony into serious work under the age of four years.

Usually, they are broken-in at three years and 'turned away '—which means put out to grass, or kept more or less to look at—until they have grown up. This is why a very young pony costs a bomb to keep. He must have proper nourishment—good grazing in summer; hay, oats, bran, and pony nuts in winter.

Vets' fees add to the expense. Every pony needs inoculating against Equine Influenza and Tetanus besides requiring proper and regular worm medicine. He also needs his own grooming kit, headcollar, leadrope, bridle and saddle, which must fit correctly for the safety of pony and rider. British ' tack', as it is called, is always the best, but expensive. Cheap foreign saddles and bridles abound but they don't last very long, and the leather soon resembles wet cardboard if you ride in the rain with it.

We broke Prince ourselves. Every day he had his lesson—catching him, grooming him lightly, lifting his feet, cleaning them out, and leading him about on his headcollar and leadrope where he could see traffic without being frightened by it.

The work had to be thoroughly done; slow and gradual, so that he would remember and associate firm, kind training with outings for him down the lanes to see things like cows clustered round a field gate, the local bus, a tractor, his first combine-harvester.

By the time he was four years old, he was as steady as a rock in all kinds of traffic, good to handle in any situation, docile with other animals, and had a lovely personality.

We got the shock of our lives when Prince suddenly fell ill. He couldn't stand one morning, although he was perfectly all right the night before. The Vet was puzzled and asked his partner to have a look at the pony. The two men shook their heads. They didn't know what was wrong with the piebald that we had saved from slaughter.

He was ill for a long time.

We propped straw bales against his back, held buckets of mash or bowls of oats and nuts beneath his nose. He ate, and drank, and every day we had to roll him over on his back and heave him onto his other side to prevent ' bed sores.' The Vets came every other day with powders, injections, advice. They did tests. All they could tell us at the end of three weeks was that it was a mystery illness caused by a virus. They could not even say if Prince would be all right again.

It was heartbreaking for us to watch the pony trying to do as we wanted, eating and drinking, allowing us to roll him over in an undignified way. People offered advice, and some said he'd never get up. We would have had him put down if he had been suffering, but he seemed to be in no pain.

His recovery was just as mysterious as the onset of the illness. One morning he simply stood up and came to the door of his loosebox to greet us. The little crossbred pony had beaten death again.

He taught a great many friends to ride after he had fully recovered.

Sadly, I outgrew Prince and we had to sell him. He went to the owners of a riding school for their own children to ride. We, who had loved him so, and learned so much from him, cried after he had gone.

A few days later, we went off to the sale yards to save yet another good pony from being slaughtered for meat. Although I love my new pony just as much, somehow I'll never forget Prince, my little meat-pie pony.

THE END.

There is nothing more traditional than the bridal veil. Long ago it was thought that evil spirits might be present to harm the bride and groom, so the bride wore a veil to hide her from the spirits.

WEDDING TRADITIONS

Bridesmaids were chosen from girls of her own age who surrounded her and made it more difficult for the spirits to single her out.

The trousseau custom began because a girl needed a completely different set of clothes to mark her married status.

It is only after the marriage vows have been taken that the bride raises her veil. But there is one exception—royal brides leave their faces uncovered throughout the ceremony. This comes from the times when a royal marriage meant a political alliance, and a switch of brides could have been part of a plot against a country.

The role of the best man now is that of the ring bearer and odd-job man—but, before, he had a much tougher role. His function goes back to primitive times when "marriage by capture" was common. A man would call on his friends to help him while he carried off his bride, who had usually consented.

Since Roman times, the holiday of the happy couple has been called "Honeymoon." It was said that the couple's affection had reached its height at the wedding ceremony and would afterwards wane like the moon. They were then given honey as a symbol of sweetness.

The tradition of carrying a bride over the threshold comes from folk legend and is another way of protecting the bride from any spirits lurking about—the safest place was said to be in the arms of her husband.

But there is also the old superstition that the person who first sets foot in the house will be the one who will rule the household.

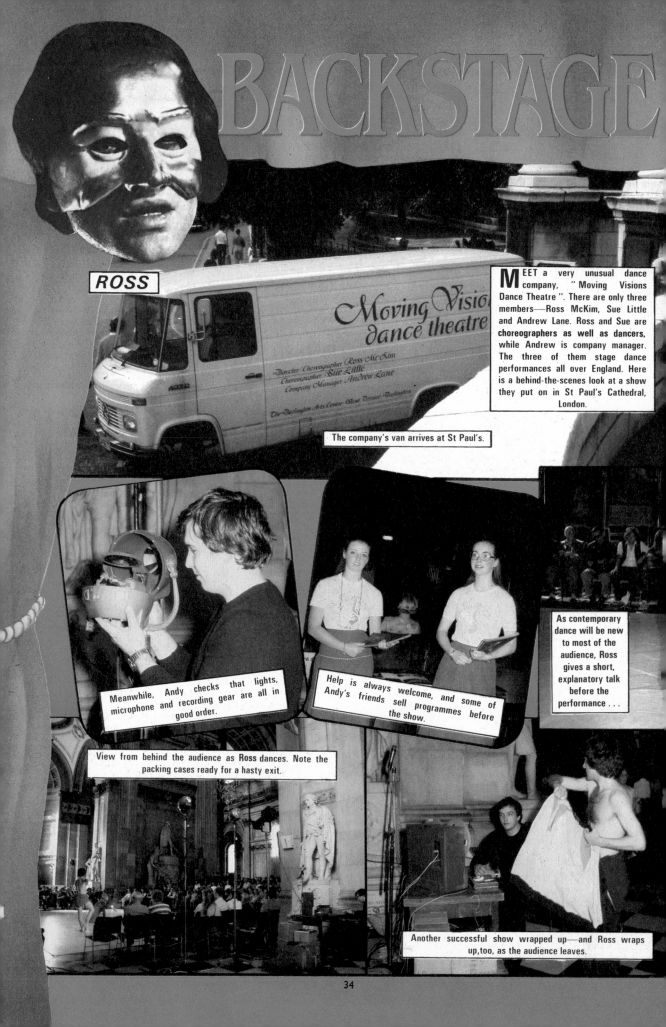

BACKSTAGE

ROSS

MEET a very unusual dance company, " Moving Visions Dance Theatre ". There are only three members—Ross McKim, Sue Little and Andrew Lane. Ross and Sue are choreographers as well as dancers, while Andrew is company manager. The three of them stage dance performances all over England. Here is a behind-the-scenes look at a show they put on in St Paul's Cathedral, London.

The company's van arrives at St Paul's.

Meanwhile, Andy checks that lights, microphone and recording gear are all in good order.

Help is always welcome, and some of Andy's friends sell programmes before the show.

As contemporary dance will be new to most of the audience, Ross gives a short, explanatory talk before the performance . . .

View from behind the audience as Ross dances. Note the packing cases ready for a hasty exit.

Another successful show wrapped up—and Ross wraps up, too, as the audience leaves.

at the DANCE

SUE

The equipment unloaded, Ross and Sue are ready for their warming-up exercises.

It's hard work, but essential to maintain muscle tone and stamina.

. . . while Sue gets her costume ready.

The show is on, and Andy must speak over the microphone besides co-ordinating lights and sound track. It takes a lot of concentration.

Now the packing-up begins.

The floor covering must be rolled up.

Andy checks that none of the expensive equipment is missing . . .

. . . then puts it carefully into boxes.

Into the waiting van with it.

Don't forget the floor covering!

Sue has a final word with a verger . . .

. . . and they're ready to get the show on the road again. It'll be a long haul, for they're booked to tour the North of England.

36

Lost Chance

TWELVE-YEAR-OLD Jenny Norton dreamed of becoming a writer, but always seemed to be in trouble for writing at the wrong moments.

This time I really must confiscate these notes you've been writing under your desk, Jenny!

Oh! Miss Roberts!

Later—

Hard luck, Jenny. Still, Miss Roberts had warned you about writing in class.

Yes, but I just couldn't wait to finish off that story I was doing, Ann.

But Jenny was determined, and, late that night—

Jenny, you really must get some sleep now. It's Saturday tomorrow . . . perhaps you can finish your story then!

At home—

I see that tomorrow is the final day for posting, Jenny. Aren't you too late to start?

DAILY NEWS

Mum, there's a talent contest advertised here: Write a story for "Girls' Weekly"! This could be my chance!

Next day, in the garden—

Only a few more lines to go. I'll get it finished in time after all.

Jenny, could you do something for me? It's urgent and I can't leave my baking at the moment.

Old Mrs Thompson has just 'phoned to ask me to get her a few things for lunch today. She's in bed with flu, so we must help her. It'll only take you minutes.

OK, Mum!

I must hurry or I'll miss the last post.

Jenny was soon back with the shoppping.

I'll just get a stamp to post my story before the final collection! I've only got ten minutes!

But when Jenny returned to the garden—

The wind has caught my manuscript!

JUDY'S Design-a-Card

Ever fancied making one of those crazy pop-up cards? Imagine making birthday cards, Christmas or Valentine cards, to your own design!

Here are three types of pop-up designs. The first is the 4-fold pop-up, which does simply that. The second is a 3-fold novelty card...the elephant's trunk swings up as you open the card! The third is a 3-fold pop-out card. Open the card and the wings—or whatever you like—pop out sideways.

These designs are, of course, just examples. You will probably have ideas of your own.

THE 4 FOLD POP-UP

Draw out your design, as suggested. Use ordinary thinnish paper for this one. In this case, you want the flowers to pop-up. Fold the card so that the cover picture—the girl's head—is behind the inside picture. Now fold as in "A". Next, score lines as in "B". Finally, push the pop-up inward as in "C". The centre fold on the pop-up must fold forward to enable the flowers to swing down into the card.

BLOW your TRUMPET!

LOVE BIRD!

Happy Valentine's Day

Pick of the BUNCH!

BEND FORWARD

A

B

C

40

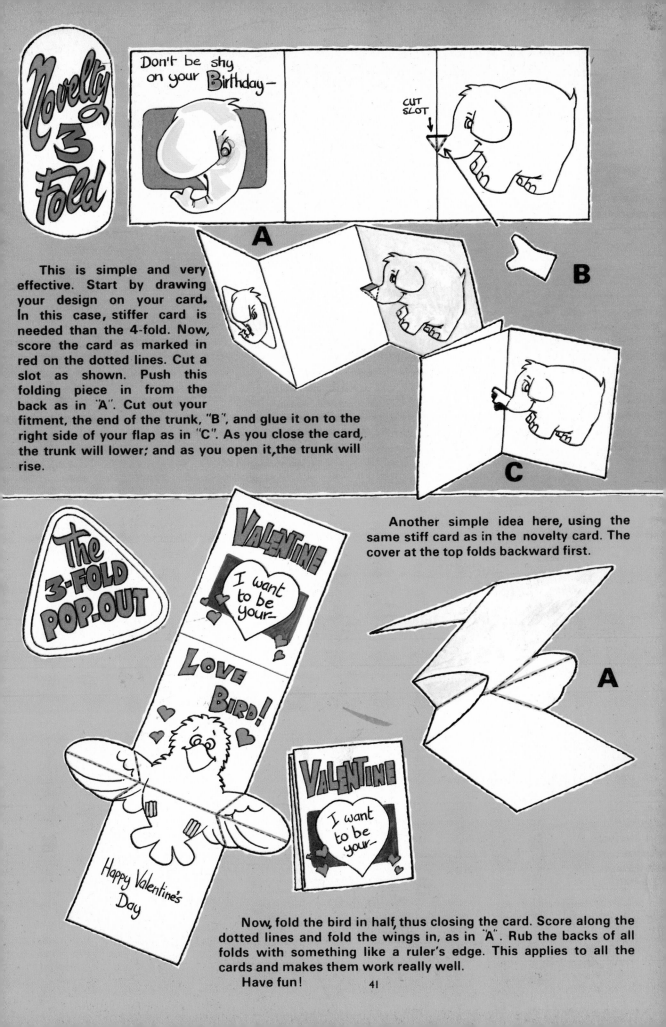

Novelty 3 Fold

Don't be shy on your Birthday —

CUT SLOT

A

B

This is simple and very effective. Start by drawing your design on your card. In this case, stiffer card is needed than the 4-fold. Now, score the card as marked in red on the dotted lines. Cut a slot as shown. Push this folding piece in from the back as in "A". Cut out your fitment, the end of the trunk, "B", and glue it on to the right side of your flap as in "C". As you close the card, the trunk will lower; and as you open it, the trunk will rise.

C

The 3-FOLD POP-OUT

VALENTINE — I want to be your—

LOVE BIRD!

Happy Valentine's Day

VALENTINE — I want to be your—

Another simple idea here, using the same stiff card as in the novelty card. The cover at the top folds backward first.

A

Now, fold the bird in half, thus closing the card. Score along the dotted lines and fold the wings in, as in "A". Rub the backs of all folds with something like a ruler's edge. This applies to all the cards and makes them work really well.

Have fun!

41

THE AFANC

BEN EVANS, a gamekeeper from the village of Llanydris in North Wales, had mysteriously disappeared. One night a police patrol car picked up a strange figure in its headlights.

It's Ben! Ben Evans! But . . . but he looks so strange! And he never rode a horse!

As suddenly as it had appeared, the figure vanished without trace. Back at the police station—

It looked like old Ben, but covered in hair and shaggy and wild-looking.

That was no mortal you saw, constable, but the Afanc, returned for his revenge!

... but vowed he'd return for his revenge.

What a load of rubbish!

The old folk-tales tell of him ... a spirit, astride a shaggy horse, that rules the Welsh forest and hunts the unwary traveller. He was lured away centuries since ...

The "Llanydris Gazette" didn't think that it was rubbish.

LLANYDRIS GAZETTE

NO 9843

1786

10 PENCE

HAS AFANC RETURNED?

And neither did Prue Lord and her friends at Llanydris Comprehensive School.

It says that people don't usually see an Afanc and live to tell the tale!

Prudence Lord! Put that newspaper away at once!

You girls would be better advised to study your text books!

But, Miss Baker, it says that .....

JUDY READERS' CALENDAR 1982

LAURA PRICE
Brixham

LORRAINE RAMAGE
Belfast

KAREN SOPER
Exeter

GEORGINA NEWEY
Sutton Coldfield

JULIE BENSON
Glasgow

MARGARET LITTLEJOHN
Tullibody

	JANUARY	FEBRUARY	MARCH
Sun.	3 10 17 24 31	7 14 21 28	7 14 21 28
Mon.	4 11 18 25	1 8 15 22	1 8 15 22 29
Tues.	5 12 19 26	2 9 16 23	2 9 16 23 30
Wed.	6 13 20 27	3 10 17 24	3 10 17 24 31
Thur.	7 14 21 28	4 11 18 25	4 11 18 25
Fri.	1 8 15 22 29	5 12 19 26	5 12 19 26
Sat.	2 9 16 23 30	6 13 20 27	6 13 20 27

	APRIL	MAY	JUNE
Sun.	4 11 18 25	2 9 16 23 30	6 13 20 27
Mon.	5 12 19 26	3 10 17 24 31	7 14 21 28
Tues.	6 13 20 27	4 11 18 25	1 8 15 22 29
Wed.	7 14 21 28	5 12 19 26	2 9 16 23 30
Thur.	1 8 15 22 29	6 13 20 27	3 10 17 24
Fri.	2 9 16 23 30	7 14 21 28	4 11 18 25
Sat.	3 10 17 24	1 8 15 22 29	5 12 19 26

	JULY	AUGUST	SEPTEMBER
Sun.	4 11 18 25	1 8 15 22 29	5 12 19 26
Mon.	5 12 19 26	2 9 16 23 30	6 13 20 27
Tues.	6 13 20 27	3 10 17 24 31	7 14 21 28
Wed.	7 14 21 28	4 11 18 25	1 8 15 22 29
Thur.	1 8 15 22 29	5 12 19 26	2 9 16 23 30
Fri.	2 9 16 23 30	6 13 20 27	3 10 17 24
Sat.	3 10 17 24 31	7 14 21 28	4 11 18 25

	OCTOBER	NOVEMBER	DECEMBER
Sun.	3 10 17 24 31	7 14 21 28	5 12 19 26
Mon.	4 11 18 25	1 8 15 22 29	6 13 20 27
Tues.	5 12 19 26	2 9 16 23 30	7 14 21 28
Wed.	6 13 20 27	3 10 17 24	1 8 15 22 29
Thur.	7 14 21 28	4 11 18 25	2 9 16 23 30
Fri.	1 8 15 22 29	5 12 19 26	3 10 17 24 31
Sat.	2 9 16 23 30	6 13 20 27	4 11 18 25

JULIE PAICE
South Ockendon

NATALIE DORAN
Glasgow

MICHELLE BUTLER
London

ALEXANDRA CUMMINGS
Withernsea

BORN TO DANCE

PAULA DELANEY, a junior assistant to ballet teacher Madame Nina Nerova, had the bright idea of inviting a TV production team to film Madame at work, in the hope that this would attract budding ballet stars to join the school.

Keep at it, girls! Paula—you're drooping!

No wonder! I'm aching all over! Madame Nerova has really put us through our paces for the cameras!

A few minutes later, Paula spoke to the cameras.

Madame Nerova is always on the lookout for new talent—so if you think you've got what it takes, come along to the auditions next week.

A few days later, at the auditions—

That TV programme has led to an amazing response.

I just hope that some have real talent!

Rodney will take your names, girls.

One at a time, girls!

They all have enthusiasm, Paula—but the born ballerina is indeed rare.

52

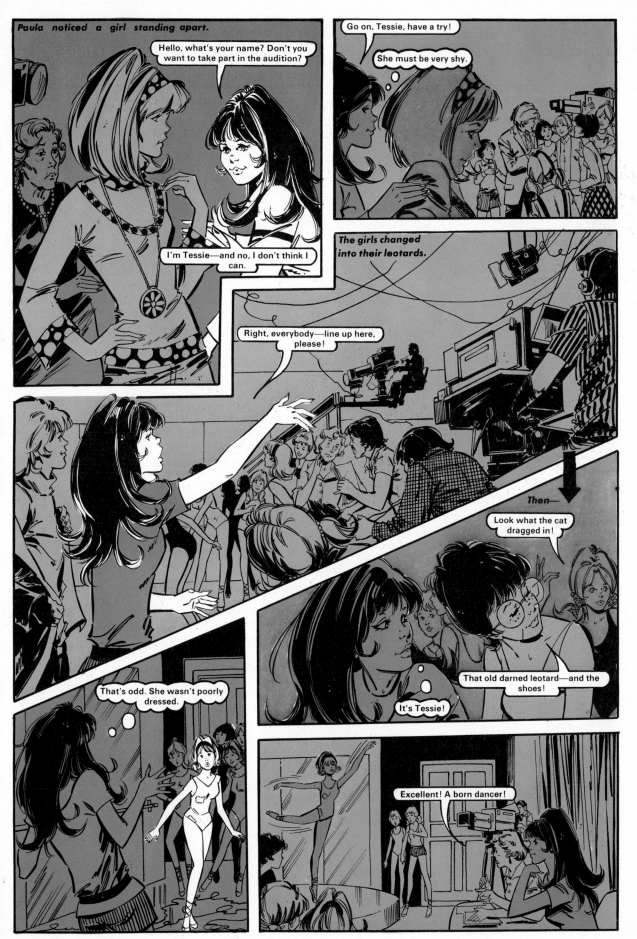

53

When the audition ended—

Paula, I didn't know we were going to be filmed! I don't want to be on TV!

But why? You danced so well!

Yes, indeed. You will be offered a place at my school. There is a great future ahead for you in ballet.

Oh, no! I can never be a dancer . . .

Next moment, Tessie vanished.

Why did the child run off like that? We must find her, Rodney!

I'm afraid we don't have her address, Madame.

Next day, Paula and Rodney, the TV producer, watched a run-through of the film.

This should be . . .

Of course! Why didn't I see it before? Excuse me, Rodney—I must dash!

Paula telephoned Madame Nerova.

Certainly I'll come, Paula— but I don't quite understand . .

I'll explain when I meet you, Madame! You won't be wasting your time, I promise!

Soon afterwards—

Why all the mystery, Paula? You still haven't told me where we're going.

We're here . . . number ten.

This is the address I found. I only hope I haven't made a mistake!

There was no mistake

Oh! How did you find me?

Who is it, Tessie?

Tessie! So this is your surprise, Paula!

Only part of it, Madame.

Madame Nerova!

Teresa Grey! My dear, I heard about your sad accident. Why did you hide yourself away from us all?

Your mother used to be my favourite pupil, Tessie.

And my favourite ballerina! I never missed one of Teresa Grey's performances. That's how I spotted the resemblance when I watched the film of Tessie dancing.

Tessie? But Tessie doesn't dance!

Yes, I do, Mum. I love dancing . . . I can't help it.

I saved my pocket-money for lessons and patched up your old ballet kit—but I never meant you to know. You were so unhappy when you knew you'd never dance again. I didn't want to bring back sad memories.

Yes, I was bitter, Tessie. I thought I'd lost everything when my career ended—but I was wrong. One day my daughter will be the star that I can never be!

Oh, Mum!

At the end of term performance—

Tessie really deserves her success. She's worked hard this term.

But she would never have had the chance at all but for you, Paula!

THE END

Dottie's

JANUARY

FEBRUARY

MAY

JUNE

SEPTEMBER

OCTOBER

s Year

MARCH

THE MARCH WINDS DID BLOW!

You can always tell when is March. There's never an bright TV aerial!

APRIL

AND AS FOR APRIL SHOWERS...

I told you to bring an umbrella, Dottie!

JULY

IN JULY, WE WENT ON A HOLIDAY TO THE COSTA LOTTA IN SPAIN.

HOLIDAY CHALETS

But you SAID you wanted your room right next to the sea!

AUGUST

IN AUGUST, UNCLE JOCK TOOK ME GROUSE SHOOTING IN SCOTLAND. HE HAD A NEW DOG.

Ho! Ho! He's really good at fetching! He's brought your slippers!

NOVEMBER

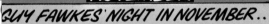

GUY FAWKES' NIGHT IN NOVEMBER...

You spent all your pocket-money on that one rocket? Sort of cash 'n' carry only— as your dad will have to set it off for you!

DECEMBER

AND, OF COURSE, THE BEST MONTH OF THE YEAR — DECEMBER.

I hope I can get this finished in time for Christmas! Dad said he'd fill my stocking with goodies!

Oh, Cora, what can I say? I guess I'd better leave you to your sorrows.

That evening, a meeting of the Palewell Seniors was called.

You all know why we're here. An action of ours—the sending of Cora Carter to Coventry two weeks ago—has resulted in the total loss of her match-making powers.

I think I speak for all of us when I say that we've come to appreciate during these last two weeks just how much we need Cora as she was.

Right! I'd never have got to know Roy if she hadn't pushed me into the swimming pool when he was competing for his hundred yards certificate.

So what we have to do is restore Cora's confidence in herself. For that, we are going to need the co-operation of two members at this meeting . . . Laura and Neil. You've got to make Cora believe she's brought you back together again.

WHAT?

You can always break up again afterwards!

All right. I am willing to put aside my personal feelings for the sake of Palewell.

Me, too.

But that's only half the battle, Pam. We've still to get Cora to *do* something to bring them together. And, from what we've heard, she's completely out of ideas.

Don't worry, I've got that under control. Now, I'll want three volunteers . . . Phil, Steve and Sally!

Later— Hi, Cora! May we come in?

Just thought we'd like to turn over a few ideas for getting Laura and Neil together.

Huh!

We've thought of a few schemes . . . of course, only *you* will know if they'll work.

All this reminds me of my cousin, Norman. He nearly lost his girl because he spent all his time messing about with his motor-boat.

Know how he got her back? By naming the boat after her. Painted the word ' NORA ' on the side of it.

Really, Sally? But never mind your cousin. Let's get back to Laura and Neil.

Pity Neil hasn't a boat to paint Laura's name on.

Yes, we could do it for him when he wasn't looking!

But we all know Neil hasn't got a boat!

What else we could paint Laura's name on?

His tennis racket?

All this fuss over a stupid bike!

That's it! That's it! Cora, you're a genius! We'll paint Laura's name on Neil's bike!

'Bye, Cora! We knew you'd come through with a brilliant idea!

What a girl!

See you later! We're going to put your suggestion into practice!

But—but what did I say?

On the day of the match—

We've no guarantee they're going to win their match. I mean, they're back together in name only. For all we know, they still loathe each other.

Somehow I doubt that! Just look over there!

Neil, do you really mean you don't want my name taken off your bike when all this is over?

That's right, Laura. I'd like to see it there every time I'm cycling on the bike.

LAURA

After that, their performance in the mixed doubles was unbeatable.

We won! We won! The cup's ours!

Well done, Palewell!

Well, I'm glad I managed to bring that off.

I wonder if that pair who played for St Cyprian's have anything going? They look to me as if they were *made* for each other, and I . . .

Hold tight, folks . . . here we go again! Cora Cupid is back to normal!

THE END

63

It's about the book, isn't it? I've been taking great care of it. I intended to bring it back tomorrow, honestly. Emma didn't know about my taking it. She thought I borrowed it from a friend.

Tell me all about it, Jill.

Jill explained that she and Emma were orphans. Emma had been a cripple all her life, and, since the death of their parents, Jill had looked after her. Emma's great interest was in painting, and, when money became scarce, Jill resorted to " borrowing " books on art to help her sister make the most of her talent.

It was wrong of me, I know, but . . .

I understand, and I'm sure you won't do it again. This is good, Emma. May I see some more of your work?

Of course.

These are great!

There! Finished!

I've tried to catch that special look you have when you smile—like the golden sun breaking through clouds.

Thanks, Emma!

I must think of a way to help.

The following morning, Anna got an interview with Mr Westerby.

Would you look at these, please? Then I'd like to tell you about the girl who did them.

I think that Westerby's could help Emma.

Let's hear your bright idea, then!

In Westerby's a few days later—

The queue is getting longer by the minute! And Emma is certainly giving her customers value for money.

ARTISTS MATERIALS

HAVE YOUR PORTRAIT DRAWN While you wait!
E. WINTERS

Yes, indeed. A most talented girl. I reckon she'll never be short of money again—thanks to you.

THE END

67

Could YOU

I'm sure you sometimes wonder what it's like to be a star. I know everyone here at `Judy´drifts off into daydreams of fame and fortune every once in a while. But how would you get on if you really did hit the big-time? Could you really be a star? Just answer these 12 questions and you'll find out!

1. If you're going to feel as fresh as a daisy, how many hours sleep do you like to have?
A. Six.
B. Ten.
C. Twenty-four.

2. Which of these meals would you like to eat most often?
A. Sausage, egg and chips.
B. Chinese nosh.
C. Mum's home-made steak and kidney pie.

3. If you were a famous pop star, how would you treat your fans? Would you:
A. Be friendly, but make sure some of your life was kept private, so you could relax every now and again.
B. Do everything to make your fans happy and never think of yourself.
C. Be rude to them and throw apple pies at any fans who dared to ask for your autograph.

4. If you want a smash hit Top Twenty record, which TV show will help you to win the most new fans?
A. Blue Peter.
B. Crackerjack.
C. Top of the Pops.

5. Imagine you're singing at a big concert, in front of 5,000 fans. Suddenly, you trip and fall flat on your face in the middle of the stage. Do you:
A. Burst into tears and run off the stage.
B. Burst out laughing and make a joke of it.
C. Blush like mad, but keep on singing.

6. A top deejay tells you he hates your latest record. Do you:
A. Smile and pretend you're not upset.
B. Tell him you think the record's great.
C. Thump him.

Be A Star?...

7. How would you describe your personality?
A. Easy-going.
B. Shy.
C. Friendly and full of confidence.

8. How do you feel about flying?
A. It's more frightening than your big sister —without her make-up.
B. It's OK, but you get tired of flapping your arms.
C. It's more exciting than watching The Hulk on TV.

9. Which would you rather do?
A. Be a soloist in the school choir.
B. Just be a member of the school choir.
C. Just watch the school choir.

10. How often do you dream of being a star?
A. Only when you're bored.
B. Nearly every day.
C. Only when you bump your head—and start seeing stars.

11. If your teacher asks you to stand up and read in front of the class, do you:
A. Feel like sinking into the floor.
B. Feel embarrassed, but try not to show it.
C. Feel flattered and try to read really well.

12. If you couldn't be a pop star, what would you like to be?
A. An elephant trainer?
B. A pop journalist.
C. Nothing. I'm going to be a star, no matter how hard I have to try?

Answers

1. A.2. B.1. C.0. 2. A.2. B.1. C.0. 3. A.1. B.2. C.0. 4. A.1. B.0. C.2. 5. A.0. B.2. C.1. 6. A.2. B.1. C.0. 7. A.1. B.0. C.2. 8. A.0. B.1. C.2. 9. A.2. B.1. C.0. 10. A.1. B.2. C.0. 11. A.0. B.1. C.2. 12. A.0. B.1. C.2.

Star-Gazer's Chart.

OVER 18—Hey! You'd better pack your bags and get ready to hit The Big - Time! You've got the confidence and determination to become a star. You realise it's hard work, but you don't mind. There will be plenty of time to enjoy life when you've climbed to the top of the pop tree. Remember us when you're famous!

12 to 18—You could make it as a star, but are you sure it's the life for you? Would you like flying all over the world, eating meals at weird times, being stared at all the time? Maybe you'd be happier in another exciting career. But if your sights are set on pop stardom, you're in with a great chance!

Under 12—You're not really the pop star type, because you don't like being the centre of attention all the time. You're like most of us, in other words! Remember, there are millions of people in the world and only a small galaxy of stars. So, you're happy to be a star-gazer!

ROCK-A-BYE

A **VERY** CUTE WAY TO PACKAGE A POSY – IN A **LACY CRADLE**.

YOU NEED: ONE PLASTIC MARGARINE TUB; THIN CARD; STICKY TAPE; LACE 7 X 50 CMS.; 'OASIS'.

1 CUT A STRIP OF THIN CARD TO THE SAME DEPTH AS YOUR PLASTIC TUB, AND MEASURE ROUND, FASTENING WITH TAPE.

STICKY TAPE

2 TAKE THE CARD 'COLLAR' OFF THE TUB, AND FASTEN A CARD STRIP 3 CMS. WIDE BY 42 CMS. LONG TO MAKE AN ARCH. THEN FASTEN THE TUB BACK INTO PLACE WITH STICKY TAPE.

3 YOU WILL NEED 50 CMS. OF LACE (OR OTHER DECORATIVE MATERIAL) 7 CMS. WIDE. FIRST COVER THE 'ARCH', GLUEING THE MATERIAL INTO POSITION. COVER THE BOTTOM PART IN THE SAME WAY.

OASIS

4 'OASIS' IS A GREEN, POROUS MATERIAL, OBTAINABLE AT FLORISTS. PLACE A BLOCK IN THE BOTTOM OF YOUR TUB.

5 CUT SHORT STEMS TO YOUR FLOWERS, SOMETHING BETWEEN 3-7 CMS. LONG. MOISTEN THE 'OASIS' AND POKE THE STEMS IN.

AND **HERE'S** THE FINISHED RESULT. IT WILL LOOK SUPER EVEN WITH WILD FLOWERS.

AND YOU CAN MAKE SIMILAR CONTAINERS TO HOLD GIFTS – JEWELLERY, SWEETS, EASTER EGGS, PERFUME, ETC.

THE RACKET

I'm sorry, Pauline. You haven't been selected for the school team this time.

Oh!

PAULINE LANGHAM was tennis mad. grandmother had en a Wimbledon mpion in the 1930's, her father had been top - class amateur yer, but somehow line could never quite make it.

And, at the local tennis court with her dad . . .

Your game isn't improving, Pauline. I beat you easily today.

Sorry, Dad. Maybe I should take up ice skating instead of tennis!

Then, one day when Pauline was tidying the attic—

Look what I've found, Dad! An old-fashioned, wooden tennis racket!

Oh, yes. That's mother's old racket —the one she used when she won Wimbledon. Why not try it out?

72

That evening, when Pauline and her father returned to their hotel—

Dad! Someone's been going through my case! My racket's gone—and the final's tomorrow!

Stay here and rest, Pauline. I'll try to get it back for you.

But Pauline could not sleep. Some hours later—

My racket! You've found it! That's great, Dad!

I've been chasing all round Rockford for this. One of the beaten competitors had taken it for spite.

The final went well for Pauline—very well.

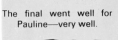

40-30! Another point and I've won the championship!

I've done it! I'm the champion!

And—

After the presentation, a reporter from the local radio station appeared.

And here's the champion herself—the girl who is taking the tennis world by storm. Can you tell our listeners the secret of your success?

That's easy! I owe it all to this old racket. It was my grandmother's. She used it when she became Wimbledon champion.

On the way home—

It's true, Dad. I'm not really a good player. The racket gives me an unfair advantage.

That isn't the real racket, Pauline! I bought it in a second-hand shop last night! And I'll tell you something else. That racket in the attic wasn't your grandmother's, either. I put it there for you to find. All you needed was confidence —and the racket gave it to you.

WOWEE! Wimbledon, here I come!

THE END

FIRST-TIME FAITH

FAITH HOPE wanted to be the girl with the most entries in a local firm's Book of Records. Now Faith was day-dreaming of the part she was to play in the Bilsea Annual Pageant and Torchlight Procession—that of Lady Bernicia, Bilsea's own heroine.

The wicked Norman Baron, Gilles de Lombardy, threatened to destroy Bilsea if the beautiful Lady Bernicia did not marry him. Though she hated him, she agreed, to save her people.

But she had refused to wear the beautiful white wedding gown he had ordered for her and, instead . . .

Oh! The Lady Bernicia's wedding gown is *black!*

I am in mourning — not only for myself, but for my poor country under Norman oppression.

Lady Bernicia's action and words caused the towns-people to revolt.

We are Saxons—not slaves of the Normans!

Aye! The Baron and his men will not take our lady!

The townspeople won the day.

The Baron was so disgraced, that the Normans never troubled our town again.

In Bilsea Museum, you can still see Lady Bernicia's white wedding dress, a symbol of resolution and courage in the face of oppression.

At the teacher's words, Faith leapt to her feet.

Miss Hunt, I've just realised . . . that dress has never yet been worn! I could create a record that would live in Bilsea's memory for years to come!

Oh, no! Here we go again!

I may leave town for Pageant Day!

Councillor Meade's running the pageant—and he's also curator of the museum. He'll love my idea. That dress is almost my size, too . . . The *first girl* to wear Lady Bernicia's wedding dress!

Councillor Meade did like the idea—but Sir George Wendel, descendant of Lady Bernicia, did not.

A schoolgirl dressed up in a family heirloom, trailing the streets in a priceless garment that can never be replaced once damaged? The answer is *no*, Mr Meade!

Later—

Mr Meade, I'd be very careful. Anyway, the dress doesn't really belong to Sir George. His family presented it to the town—so can't you insist?

I could, Faith—but he's promised a large donation for the new Youth Club, and, if we upset him, he might withdraw his offer. And now, my dear, I've got to go and dust the mummies.

And, shrugging into ancient overalls, Mr Meade went off.

Faith sought out Monica, the curator's brainy daughter.

Monica, you've heard all this fuss about Lady Bernicia's dress?

Never heard of her! Now, look, Faith—don't bother me, please. I'm working on a fascinating equation.

You're in the Netball Reserve Team, aren't you, Monica? I know you don't want to be and you'd rather work on your maths, so I'll stand in for you. All I want in return is for *you* to do *me* a little favour.

Faith's friends thought she was mad.

You mean, Monica the Swot's going to take the dress from her dad's museum and smuggle it to you?

There'll be an uproar!

Now, calm down everyone. Monica's only going to collect the dress at the last minute. And I won't be expelled, because I have Mr Meade's blessing . . .

". . . well, sort of!"

The town wants you to wear this dress, Faith—and you're resourceful. What I mean is . . . if you can find a way around the problem, the whole town will be on your side.

That had been enough for Faith.

As for Monica, she was only too delighted to get out of netball practice.

So, just before the pageant starts, I borrow Dad's keys and sneak this garment out of its case and meet you at the school with it. Right?

Right! Then I change into the dress and sail down the school steps to the float. Too late for Sir George to raise any more objections.

But, on the night of the pageant, things started to go wrong.

Now, Mr Mayor, when you give the signal, Fred will throw that switch and the Town Hall will be floodlit for the pageant.

I know! I know! You've already explained it twice! Right! There's my signal.

SNAP!

FLASH!

Every light in the town has fused!

I knew we should never have transferred Fred from the Drains and Ditches Department!

78

Meanwhile, in the museum—

This *would* happen! No lights! Fred again, I suppose! I'll have to feel my way. Now, it's three glass cases to the right, then four to the left . . . or is it four to the right and three to the left?

Later, at Bilsea High—

Now, don't fuss, girls. You're almost dressed, and the pageant itself will be by torch-light.

Faith, is that you? It's me . . . Monica!

Oh, good! Give me the dress, quickly! I just hope I can find my way into it in the dark!

The dress is not as heavy as it looks! Such an odd design.

Faith, do come on! Your ladies-in-waiting are ready!

Gosh! I feel so nervous!

Let's get hold of Faith's train. We're supposed to hold it up as she walks.

It feels ever so rough.

Well, it's covered with gold and seed pearls, you clot.

Stop yacking, will you? Now . . . one—two—three . . .

AND PAGEANT

Look at that!

Bilsea had never heard such a roar of laughter.

But what's Faith wearing?

Oh, golly! It—it's Dad's old overalls . . . the ones he keeps at the museum for when he dusts the mummies! I—I must have made a mistake in the darkness and opened his cupboard instead of the glass display case!

HA HA HA!
HOO HOO HO HA
HA H

Where . . . is . . . she? WHERE . . . IS . . . MONICA?

Tell her I'm not here! Tell her I've gone home!

You know, Phil, the way this pageant's shaping up, there's one thing you can say about it . . .

GRR!

I know, Simon . . . that it'll live in Bilsea's memory for years to come!

LET ME AT HER! LET . . . ME . . . AT . . . HER . . . !

THE END

79

PONY TALES

A CORRECT SEAT IS FUNDAMENTAL. IT IS DESIGNED TO PUT YOU IN A POSITION WHERE YOUR WEIGHT WILL BE LEAST DISTURBING, THE MAIN ONES BEING THE **DRESSAGE** SEAT AND THE **JUMPING** SEAT.

THESE ARE SIMPLY ACCOMPLISHED BY LENGTHENING (DRESSAGE) OR SHORTENING (JUMPING) THE STIRRUP LEATHERS.

IN THE **DRESSAGE**, THE RIDER SITS ERECT LIKE THIS, TALL ABOVE THE SADDLE - FIGURATIVELY SPEAKING - AND TALL BELOW.

BUT IN THE **JUMPING** SEAT, THE SHORT STIRRUPS WILL QUITE NATURALLY CONCERTINA THE RIDER, MAKING SHARP - **OW!** - ANGLES AT HIP, KNEE, AND ANKLE.

WITH HANDS FORWARD AND REINS SHORTER, **CLOSE** TO THE SADDLE DURING THE APPROACH...

...AND - **ERK!** - OVER THE ACTUAL JUMP! HOPE I GET CLEANED UP IN TIME FOR SCHOOL!

Later, at the bus stop—

YOU'RE RIGHT! THERE'S TOO MUCH SQUABBLING ON THE SCHOOL BUS...

...SO WE'LL GO TO SCHOOL...

...ON PERCY!

BUT IT'S NO USE...

...WE STILL FIGHT...

...OVER WHO'S GOING TO SIT AT THE BACK!

The GOLDEN TOUCH

MAY FARRIER'S father worked on the estate of Lady Mesham. Her family was poor, so it was a surprise to Constable Phillips to see May with a precious box late one night.

What's all this, May?

Constable Phillips! You fair startled me there! 'Tis buried treasure I found!

Buried treasure nothing, May! This jewellery was stolen from Lady Mesham up at the hall last winter! How did you know it was buried just here?

By the following day, the news was all over the village.

I know what they're all saying!

Stole Lady Mesham's jewels, her father did!

At the Farriers' cottage—

I'm sorry, Tom, but you must come with me to the station. How did May know exactly where to dig if you didn't tell her?

I just sort of guessed, Constable Phillips! Honestly!

Later—

There's a lawyer coming to see you in the morning, Tom.

Aye, George, so they tell me.

Next day, Giles Wilson, a local solicitor, visited Tom Farrier.

I've known you all my life, Tom! You'd never steal anything!

Aye—but who's going to believe me? My May *knew* the box was buried there and that's all there is to it!

Mr Wilson interviewed May.

I walked across the field, and sort of . . . felt it. So I went back that night, Mr Wilson.

You felt it? Exactly what do you mean, May?

In due course, Tom Farrier came before the magistrates, and the chief magistrate was Lady Mesham herself.

With respect to your worships, I submit that the chief magistrate should not sit on this case.

Nonsense, Mr Wilson! Unless you want this matter to drag on all day, I suggest you begin!

The hearing did not go well.

So you have no alibi? No one can vouch for your movements on the night of the robbery?

I'm afraid not, my lady.

Then Tom's solicitor had an idea.

Once May Farrier is out of the court, I think I may be able to demonstrate something.

I hope you are not wasting our time, Mr Wilson!

Giles took a gold sovereign from his watch-chain.

I am hiding the sovereign inside this book. Now, please allow Miss Farrier back into the court.

May, will you approach the bench and tell me if anything unusual strikes you?

May went to the book.

There's something gold hidden in this book, Mr Wilson.

Thank you, May!

I submit that, in fact, Miss Farrier is a diviner. Many people can detect gold—and that is how she found the treasure!

Rubbish, Mr Wilson! This has quite obviously been arranged in advance! Is there anything further before the bench retires?

Timidly, May approached the bench.

I didn't know before—but I think he's right, m'lady. And I can tell, too, that you have gold about your person.

Anyone who knows me, girl, will vouch for the fact that I never wear gold!

Suddenly, a voice rang out.

With respect to the bench, Lady Mesham, you do have gold about you!

As your dentist, Lady Mesham, I feel I must tell the court that you have four gold fillings in your teeth! The young girl *IS* plainly a deviner!

The bench retired and, when they returned—

It is our judgment that you are innocent of the charges laid against you, and, further to this . . .

. . . we recommend that a substantial reward be paid to Miss May Farrier for discovering the hiding place of the stolen goods! The court is adjourned!

THE END

87

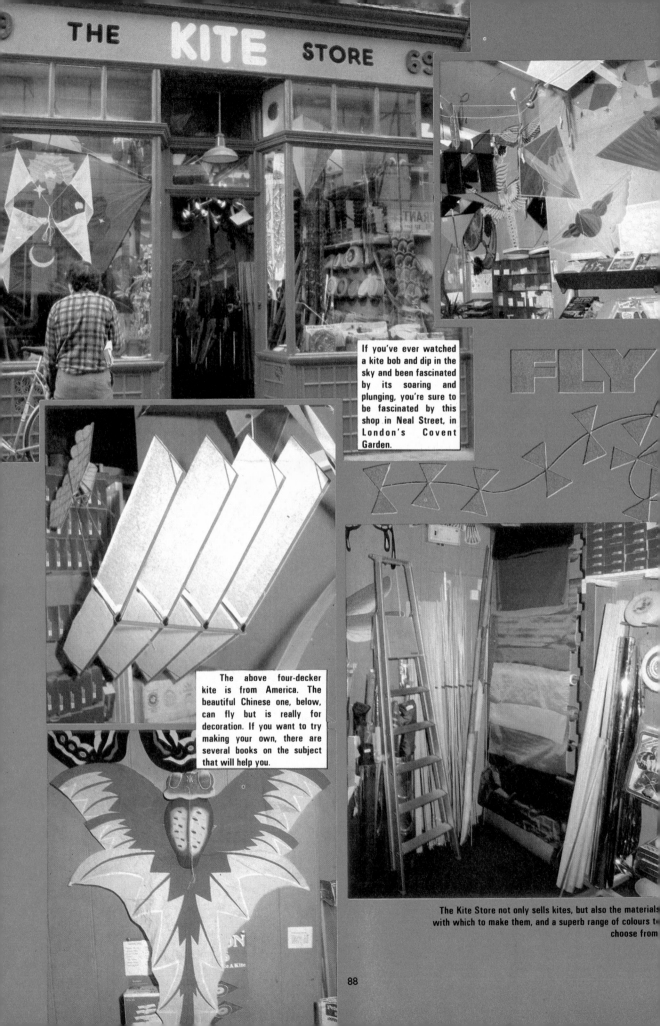

THE KITE STORE 69

If you've ever watched a kite bob and dip in the sky and been fascinated by its soaring and plunging, you're sure to be fascinated by this shop in Neal Street, in London's Covent Garden.

The above four-decker kite is from America. The beautiful Chinese one, below, can fly but is really for decoration. If you want to try making your own, there are several books on the subject that will help you.

The Kite Store not only sells kites, but also the materials with which to make them, and a superb range of colours to choose from

Inside it's a riot of colour, with kites of all sizes and designs . . .

A KITE

Kites come from as far away as India, Formosa and the Caribbean.

The Kite Store also has a collection of Frisbees, Flying Discs and Boomerangs. It is a colourful paradise for anyone who loves things that fly.

In China, the ninth day of the ninth month is kites day. It is said that, on that day, evil spirits that might attack the owner are flown away on the kite.

There is a legend that, many hundreds of years ago, a man dreamed that he was going to suffer a misfortune on a particular day. On that day, he took his family out to a high hill and flew a kite to keep himself happy. When he returned home, he found his house destroyed and his animals burned to death in the ruins. Kites day celebrates the saving of the family.

WINTER WARMERS

MATERIALS. Patons Beehive Double Knit.
Hat. 1(1) 50 gr. ball.
Scarf. 2(2) 50 gr. balls.
Keep ball bands for washing and pressing instructions.
Pair of 4 mm. (size 8) knitting needles.

MEASUREMENTS. To fit ages 6/7 (8/9) years.
It is essential to work to the stated tension. Buy the full amount at one time to avoid variations in dye lots.

TENSION. 9½ sts. and 19 rows = 5 cm. over garter st.

ABBREVIATION. K = knit; sts = stitches; tog = together; rep = repeat; mm. = millimetres; cm. = centimetres.

HAT

With 4 mm. needles cast on 85(92) sts.
Work in garter st. (every row K, first row is right side).
Work until hat measures 17(18) cm. from commencement, ending with a wrong side row.
Shape crown.
1st row. *K5, K2 tog, rep from * to the last st, K1. 73(79) sts.
Work 3 rows.
5th row. *K4, K2 tog, rep from * to the last st. K1. 61(66) sts.
Continue in this way having 1 st less between decreases on every 4th row until 25(27) sts remain.
Work 1 row.
Next row. K2 tog to the last st, K1.13 (14) sts.
Break yarn, leaving enough to thread through st. Draw up and fasten off.
Sew seam, reversing it for 7 cm. from cast on edge.

SCARF

With 4 mm. needles cast on 32 sts.
Work in garter st. for 127 cm., or required length.
Cast off.

Goodnight—and thanks!

Lucky the others didn't see me so scared! I'll have a laugh at their expense tomorrow at school.

No need to thank me, my dear. Just stop and think before you panic next time! Goodnight.

And she did!

And it was a poor little puppy, that's all. I carried it to the vicar's house.

Well, I have to admit you're braver than I am, Petra!

Me, too!

But, during the lunch-hour—

My maths homework for this afternoon . . . it's not here! I must have left it in the kitchen at the vicarage!

But when she reached the vicarage—

Oh! It looks as if it's not been lived in for years!

If I hurry, I've just time to fetch it before afternoon school starts.

94

Midnight Garden

Dreaming of fresh flowers is always lucky; but if the blooms are wilted, high hopes are doomed to disappointment!

Here are some meanings given to flowers and plants you may see, get, or gather in the garden of dreams.

Daffodils.
A very lucky dream if you're ill, since it means you'll soon feel better.

Dandelions.
Gathering these in dreamland means Mr Postman will bring you a letter in the morning mail.

Buttercups, Carnations, Daisies, Forget-me-nots.
All these are symbols of sincere and loving friendships.

Dahlias.
A friend's success will please you.

Evergreens.
Lasting love and happiness, especially if they are growing before your very eyes. But if you are scratched by holly leaves, someone will annoy you.

Jessamine.
Someone is having loving dreams about YOU!

Heather.
A journey will lead to good luck.

Mistletoe.
A handsome boyfriend.

Lilac.
A surprise invitation.

Pansies.
Very good luck. If you've been feeling anxious, and dream someone is giving you a bunch of pansies – your problems will soon be solved.

Orange Blossom.
News of a wedding.

Shamrocks.
You will cross water. So wear your wellies to school as there may be puddles about!

Roses.
A super dream, foretelling love, success, happiness and all sorts of goodies. Even wilted roses mean success with a spice of danger!

Tulips.
Do not judge people by their appearance alone.

Violets.
Romantic happenings.

Wild Flowers.
Gathering these means exciting adventures.

Sprinkling a little delicate flower scent, such as rosewater, on your pillow might help bring those lucky dreams. But go easy on the perfume. Too much could pep up your senses and keep you awake, so avoid spicey or musky blends.

ABANDONED!

AT the Morningside Children's Home, "The Emma Report," a children's news programme, was eagerly awaited.

The latest report was from a big zoo.

Mr Johnson, the zoo vet, is going to show us some of the latest patients. Oops! Let go of the mike, Nellie!

We've brought Algy in for a dental check-up, Emma.

Wow! I wouldn't fancy tinkering with an alligator's teeth!

This little tiger cub cost us a few sleepless nights, but he seems to be thriving now.

He's beautiful!

After the programme ended—

And now for the special visitor I told you about . . .

Emma!

99

Later—

Matron—Janey's disappeared! And her money-box is empty!

A search party was immediately organised.

Anything I can do to help, Matron?

Thank you, Emma, but we mustn't keep you. Janey can't be far away.

Rodney Mair, the producer of Emma's show, had come to collect her.

I just don't understand it, Rodney. Janey seemed . . .

Hey! We've got a stowaway!

Janey!

I'm sorry! I-I needed help, and I didn't know what else to do. Please, Emma, could you take me to the zoo man? I've got some money, and . . .

Suppose you tell us exactly what this is all about, Janey.

A few minutes later, in a wood near the Home—

Thank you for coming back with me. It's not far from here.

This is Patch. She's a stray. I found her with her paw badly hurt, but I bandaged it and now it's getting better.

100

WHAT AN IDEA!

The very first yo-yos weren't toys—no way! The idea came from a Filipino fighting weapon of the 16th Century, which weighed four pounds. Jungle warriors swung it on a twenty foot long thong, delivering knock-out blows to their enemies. Yet the word yo-yo doesn't mean "go-go", as you might expect, but "come-come"!

Early television sets had small black and white pictures enclosed in big, bulky surrounds—but everyone marvelled at being able to see what was happening in London. They never dreamed that, in time to come, they would see what was happening on the Moon as well! And in colour, too!

Ballpoint pens were bad news for blotting-paper manufacturers, because ink now dried almost instantly. The new-style pen could be used to sign not only the top copy, but the carbon copies underneath at one go, which saved a lot of time for shopkeepers writing receipts and so on. Of course, ballpoints have always been great for school-work, too. No more inky fingers—unless, of course, your ballpoint happens to leak!

The juke box, by the way, is also called the corn box, 'cos so many of the fave records have always been romatic ballads. Looks like that golden corn box is making a big comeback along with frilly petticoats, and full skirts that swing and swirl when you rock 'n' roll, so here come those happy days. There's a chance Mum will enjoy giving you a few jiving lessons, too!

The first crossword puzzle appeared in the New York Herald in December 1913, to amuse readers after their Christmas dinner. The person who made up this very first crossword preferred to remain anonymous, but the craze really caught on and now those teasing puzzles appear in nearly every newspaper.

Believe it or not, kids didn't always need money to get into the movies. In some cinemas the Saturday matinee customers handed over glass jam or jelly jars, instead! Each jar was worth a few pence, which was the price of a seat, and the jam manufacturers arranged to collect them from the cinemas, which must have looked more like Crystal Palaces than Picture Palaces!

The first vending machines to appear in London were fixed to the lamp-posts supporting sizzling gas lights, and they contained hot water. Not for tea-making, though. London cab drivers put a penny in the slot when they wanted to fill one of the stone hot-water bottles which kept their hansom cabs cosy.

Girls of the past spoke of ' papering their hair ', which meant rolling it round twists of paper to make curls. This took a lot of time, both at night and in the morning, but was probably better for the hair than the first curlers, which were made of metal and caused split ends. So, in the 1930's, lots of girls opted for a perm—even though making waves meant a five-hour session at the hairdressers for starters, wired up to complicated electrical equipment! And, afterwards, regular setting was necessary to keep permed waves and curls in place.

When Dr Kellogg told people he had dreamed up a new breakfast dish, he wasn't joking. He saw a method of flaking corn in a dream, and tried it out when he woke up.

Cornflakes and the cereals that followed them were not his first inventions. He had already become famous for rusks called zwiebacks—meaning ' twice baked '. Babies loved to cut their teeth on them—but they weren't so good for false teeth, as one of Dr Kellogg's patients discovered. She was an old lady who broke a false tooth on a zwieback and charged Dr Kellogg ten dollars to have her denture repaired!

MISS MATCH!

UNTIL recently, Lorna Manley and I had nothing in common—except a tendency to spots, and that's something we could share with anyone!

Lorna was clever, and usually first in the exams. I was usually first in the hundred metres—so, as exams are usually considered more important than sports events, Lorna's achievements were more significant than mine.

Lorna was eleven, four months older than I was then. She was tall, with dark hair which she pinned back with large, white hairgrips. She wore steel-rimmed specs—not because they were the current fashion at that time. You might think she would have looked awful, but she didn't. She looked competent and sure of herself . . . and she was.

She was always correcting everything I said.

"It's not 'these things over there '," she would say. "It's 'those things '."

What was more annoying, she was usually right.

I was small with curly hair.

Mum said that I had a glass-lined stomach because I could eat anything with no ill-effects—from budgie seed to chewing my pencil down to a stump during exams.

But the thing that made me *sick* was that Lorna was Miss Clapperton's favourite, and I would have given *anything* to be that.

Miss Clapperton was our form mistress. She was long-leggedly tall, with golden - red hair that bounced when she walked, and wore the most fabulous clothes. Both Lorna and I admired her and wished we could be exactly like her when we grew up. (Of course, secretly, we knew it was impossible.)

I lived near Miss Clapperton and often met her at the end of the street leading to the school and walked the short distance with her—much to Lorna's annoyance.

JOHN, my brother, was 21 and didn't speak to me often because he was always rushing to meet someone.

In the mornings, if he went off

to work without eating his breakfast , I guessed that another of his romances had come to an end. He seemed to have a lot of bad luck with his love life, for I often had to eat his bacon and egg. They would have been wasted otherwise. (Not that I'm complaining!)

I suppose I would never have thought of introducing John to Miss Clapperton if Lorna hadn't been so nasty to me at school one day.

"Miss Clapperton wants me to enter for the essay competition. Did she ask you?" Lorna asked me, knowing perfectly well what the answer would be.

Miss Clapperton knew my limitations. My punctuation was terrible.

"I don't know why you waste Miss Clapperton's time walking to school with her." Lorna was working up to being really nasty. "What on earth do you talk about? You can't have much to say to her."

That made me hopping mad.

"We talk about all sorts of

things . . . like . . . the kind of trees that grow in our garden."

"Trees?" Lorna's tone of voice should have warned me that she was moving in for the kill. "You don't have any real trees in your garden . . . only a dead Christmas tree in a tub."

I knew that Lorna was right. I looked at her straight and said:

"Look, four-eyes, just get this," remembering a bit out of the western I had seen on TV the night before, "Miss Clapperton and my brother are walking out together." (I got that bit from the movie, too. "Walking out" sounded as if it were more serious.)

Lorna's eyes nearly popped right through her glasses. Her mouth curled and she snapped "Rubbish!" and walked away.

I was left standing. I didn't think somehow that I had won that battle. I also knew that I had to do something quick to get Miss Clapperton and John "walking out" together.

JOHN was between affairs of the heart at the moment, so I thought it might be a good time to arrange for them to meet.

I spent the next few days wondering just how to do this, but I found that some things just happen by themselves without a push from anyone.

One morning, John was having breakfast when I rushed into the room, grabbed a piece of toast and ran into the hall for my coat.

"If you wait a sec. I'll give you a lift," John called. He was obviously in a good humour.

"You have egg on your mouth," I said flatly.

John used the back of his hand to wipe it off.

He couldn't meet Miss Clapperton for the first time with egg on his mouth.

"Now you've smeared it. And clean your teeth," I added as he went into the bathroom.

John doesn't usually like to be told to clean his teeth—especially by me – so when I heard him gargling, I just knew that this was my lucky day. Miss Clapperton would be at the end of the street; I felt it in my bones.

Sure enough, there at the end of the street was Miss Clapperton. I poked John and asked him to stop and give her a lift.

"She's almost at the school." John protested. "She'll think I'm mad."

"Go on . . . no . . . I mean stop," I felt breathless with excitement.

I could see John hesitating.

We stopped.

John has a sports car, and I had insisted—much to John's annoyance—on sitting in the back seat. Well, it's not a back seat, really . . . it's the boot and hard as bricks—but it meant that Miss Clapperton could sit beside John. I thought I had made rather a crafty move.

She looked amused when John stopped, then, after a short hesitation, she got in. I had forgotten that the springs in the front seat had gone, and she sat down with a thump. She laughed—but not as if she found it funny.

It was a pity that it was not very far to school. John never speaks much anyway in the morning, so we travelled in silence. Not that it's easy to speak in his car—the engine is so noisy.

Miss Clapperton seemed glad when we arrived at the school gates. I was glad, too, but for a different reason. I had seen Lorna arriving at the school in her sister's car, and I knew that she would see Miss Clapperton get out of John's car.

"Is that Joan Manley driving her sister to school?" John seemed to have forgotten all about Miss Clapperton.

"Yes," I said. She takes Lorna to school most days."

"Didn't know Joan could drive," John said.

So what was all the fuss about Joan Manley being able to drive?

I thought that John got out of his car with indecent haste, hardly waiting for Miss Clapperton to swing her elegant legs out of the low seat. He did not even open the door and help her out. He leapt out and went towards Joan Manley's car.

As Miss Clapperton walked towards the school gates, I realised for the first time how really tall she was—about a head taller than John.

Lorna and I went into the school together. She seemed in a good humour. She did not say anything about seeing Miss Clapperton come out of John's car and surprised me by inviting me to come along to the Chess Club with her. She said that I might make quite a good chess player. Lorna did not show any surprise when I told her that I used to play chess with John.

I wonder if she had known before? Maybe Lorna should be a medium.

THAT day I could do nothing right and Miss Clapperton called me an idiot several times—and sounded as if she meant it.

I began to regret that I had introduced her to John. If they did have a romance, it would be terrible if they quarrelled. I could imagine Miss Clapperton sending messages—nastily subtle ones—through me to John; and I still had two terms to do in her year.

I didn't feel lucky any more—except that Lorna shared her bar of chocolate with me at break because I had forgotten mine. She was really nicer than I thought . . .

John is engaged!

It happened very quickly and took me by surprise—but not my family. I can't think how I missed out on this; everyone else took it as a natural course of events.

What I had not known was that John used to take Lorna's sister Joan out occasionally, and, when they met outside the school, John began dating her again.

John has gone all gaga over Joan. I overheard him telling her that she looked gorgeous. I wonder why he did not see that when he first took her out?

People must change.

Anyway, now they are engaged and John is eating huge breakfasts every day and there are never any left-overs for me. Lorna has become my best friend and she is helping me with my punctuation.

I have gone off Miss Clapperton a bit as she has bought a red sports car for herself, and she often passes me on the way to school and *never* stops to pick me up—even on the wettest of days!

THE END

BOBBY DAZZLER was the only girl at Westbury Boarding School for boys, where her mother was matron. There was even fiercer rivalry than usual between her two admirers, Mike Norton and Don Carter, when Bobby was given two tickets for the local youth club disco— one for herself and one for her chosen partner.

BOBBY DAZZLER

It's no use squabbling over the ticket, you two. Somehow we've got to sort this out sensibly.

Whatever I do, it looks like one of them's in for a disappointment.

Next morning—

I've cleaned your shoes for you, Bobby.

How nice of you, Mike.

Then—

Hey! These were once my best brown shoes—not that anyone would notice now that you've cleaned them with *black* polish!

Oh! S—sorry, Bobby!

Later —

I'll carry that tray for you, Bobby!

Don!

Oh!

Hah! That's spoiled Don's chances!

Each as bad as the other! They ought to be practising for the big football match against Oakley School. Wait a minute . . . that gives me an idea.

Bobby explained her plan to Mike and Don.

Today's only Sunday, so you've plenty of time to practise. Whoever scores the most goals next Saturday afternoon will come to the disco with me in the evening. I can't think of anything fairer than that.

Next day, after school—

That goal-scoring contest was quite a brainwave. With all this training, those two should be on top form by Saturday—and Westbury's never beaten Oakley School yet.

Bobby! You're wanted on the telephone!

Coming, Mum!

A few seconds later—

That's fine by me, Dave. I'll go and tell Don and Mike right away.

But as Bobby approached the field—

Phew! I'm exhausted! If it weren't for Bobby's idea, you wouldn't find me slogging away like this all the time!

Huh! Do you think I'd be practising here if it wasn't for the disco?

If that's how you feel, I'll keep my news to myself after all!

On Saturday afternoon—

Fantastic! That plan of mine worked wonders! Mike's scored two goals—but that's Don's third!

And, just before the final whistle—

Hooray! Another goal from Mike—and Westbury's won!

So much for your precious plan, Bobby! We scored three goals each—so who gets the disco ticket?

You can hardly split it in half!

I can do better than that, Don.

Dave from the youth club 'phoned on Monday. They're short of boys for tonight's disco evening—and he offered me another free ticket to help make up even numbers.

You've known about this since Monday—and let us put in all that football practice for nothing?

Not for nothing, Mike! Thanks to that practice, Westbury won the match—and that means we've an extra special reason for celebrating this evening!

THE END

NATTY NAPKIN RINGS

A Christmas dinner table always looks good when it's laden with goodies, but these pretty napkin rings can add that little extra special touch.

YOU WILL NEED:

Cardboard rolls (Depending on the number of people having the meal).

Foil wrapping paper, in any colour of your choice.

1 roll of self-adhesive gift wrap ribbon, in contrasting colour to foil.

1 tube of glue.

TO MAKE NAPKIN RING

1. Cut a length of cardboard roll 75 mm. (3″) long (the inside of a toilet roll is ideal).

2. Cut a piece of foil 75 mm. (3″) wide by 150 mm. (6″) deep. Wrap the paper round the roll and glue into position.

TO MAKE BOW

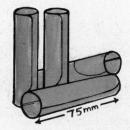

1. Cut 4 strips of ribbon 150 mm. (6″) long. Fold in half. Moisten ends and press to centre.

2. Moisten back of one loop and press on to second in criss-cross pattern.

3. Moisten others till you get this shape.

4. Cut small piece of ribbon 25 mm. (1″) long to make a roll to press into centre of flower.

Your flower is now ready to attach to the napkin ring.

SCHOOLGIRL VET

KAY BURROWS hoped one day to be a vet like her brother, David. She was thrilled when a Chinese girl came to stay with their family while a convention of veterinary surgeons was being held in a nearby seaside town.

Miss Soong, I'm looking forward to your lecture tomorrow on treating animals by acupuncture.

Acupuncture? Sticking needles in them?

Really, Mum! You make it sound like witchcraft! It's a serious medical science and the Chinese pioneered it.

If it works on human beings, why not on animals?

In my lecture, I shall give examples of my own successes with cats and dogs.

It'll be interesting to see the reaction of my senior partner, Duncan Mackenzie! He's so old-fashioned, he'll probably have a fit!

A little later, Kay's friend, Lucy, came for a final rehearsal for the school concert.

Kay has great musical talent, Mrs Burrows. Will she make it her career?

I'd like her to, but her heart is set on becoming a vet.

The following morning—

Miss Soong is coming with me on my morning round. I've left a list beside the 'phone of the addresses I'll be visiting.

A little later—

The Elworthys are retired farmers, but they still keep one cow, Blossom—she's really just a pet.

Inside the cowshed—

Blossom has gone lame. I've been treating her myself, but she's not any better so I thought I'd better call you.

What treatment have you been giving her?

109

HOME COOKING

TALK about getting out of bed on the wrong side! I just knew it was going to be one of those days from the minute I got up and plunged my feet right into the bowl of soggy cornflakes I'd brought for supper and then not fancied.

As I hopped crossly across the landing to the bathroom to clean up, I remembered what day it was. Wednesday—cookery day. No wonder I'd woken up feeling so cross.

"I hate Wednesdays," I muttered. "I hate Domestic Science, and I hate Miss Woodward, and I absolutely loathe cooking."

And I squeezed the toothpaste so hard that a striped worm shot out all over the floor.

By the time I'd cleared up the mess, Mum was yelling up the stairs that breakfast was ready, so I had one mad dash to get dressed and make my bed.

"Now then, love, Wednesday today," said Mum, glancing at the calendar. "What do you need for cookery?"

I sighed with frustration. If only she'd forget just once.

"I've got the list in my satchel," I mumbled.

"That's nice," said Mum cheerfully when she'd read it, then she looked at Dad. "Savoury pie this time, Harry. You'll like that won't you?"

Dad peered round his newspaper and grinned.

"Fine," he said, but I saw him wink at Mum.

I sighed again. It was the same old routine every week. Each Wednesday teatime the rest of the family pretended to enjoy my soggy sponges, granite rock cakes and cardboard tarts.

"Must dash," I called, grabbing the carrier bag Mum handed me. "See you!"

The bus was just coming as I reached the stop and, as usual, the boys piled on first. "Gosh! I wish there was just one other girl here," I thought for the hundredth time. It was just my luck that I was the only girl from our school to get on at this stop.

By the time the cookery lesson actually came round, I'd got myself into a real state. The trouble was that all the other girls actually liked cooking, and couldn't wait to get on those silly hairbands and aprons and make a start. They thought I was odd.

We started by making the pastry case and, as usual, my fat wouldn't mix in with the flour properly.

"Bread-crumb-sized lumps, Jane," Miss Woodward remarked sarcastically. "Not clay chunks!"

I felt like throwing the whole lot at her.

By the time I'd rolled out the pastry and lined my pie dish ready, the others were already frying their bacon and onions and mushrooms. That really smelt quite appetizing, but then I burnt my hand on some hot fat and sent what seemed to be a hundred mushrooms rolling on to the floor, and it lost its appeal.

It took me ages to clear that up, then I still had to beat up the egg and milk to pour over the pie filling. The others were all washed up and making notes before my pie even went in the oven.

"Very nice, Sally," approved Miss Woodward at the end of the lesson, marching like a sergeant-major up and down the rows of pies laid out for her inspection. "A little bit lop-sided, Fay. Just a bit too brown, Pat."

And so she went on down the line. When she got to mine, hastily shoved at the end not two minutes before, she stopped and put her hands on her hips. I waited.

"Untidy, overdone, pastry texture too crumbly..., and you forgot to slice tomatoes on the top, Jane," she commented quickly. "Never mind, we can't all be cordon-bleus, can we?"

I felt like telling her that not all of us wanted to be, but I didn't bother because, at least, it was all over for another week and time to go home.

Ten minutes later I subsided thankfully on to an empty seat on the bus and sat brooding over the unfairness of girls having to cook.

"Hey, what's that smell?" a voice shouted behind me, and I turned to find Tim Marsh staring at my carrier bag.

"Nothing," I said quickly.

"Smells fabulous," said his friend Lenny. "You've been cooking, Jane. What did you make?"

"Savoury pie," I muttered uncomfortably, hoping I wasn't in for a session of teasing from the boys now.

"Let's see."

"C'mon, let's have a look."

Before I could stop him, Tim had taken my pie out of the bag and was holding it up. I closed my eyes in despair, but then opened them again almost at once when I heard him say, "That's fantastic, Jane. I didn't know you were good at cooking."

My mouth opened in astonishment.

"I s'pose you couldn't spare a bit?" Tim grinned appealingly at me. "I'm ravenous."

"So am I," said the others at once.

"Well..." I was so staggered at having a bit of real praise for once that I didn't know what to say.

"Gosh, thanks," Tim said eagerly, taking my silence to mean yes, and in no time at all he'd broken off four pieces.

There was a silence while they all munched enthusiastically and I held my breath.

"Super," said Larry.

"I like a bit of home cooking," agreed Tim. "I seem to get nothing but those instant tasteless foods at home."

"Same here," said Lenny. "This is really great."

"I wish Mum had time to cook like this," added Roger.

A glow of satisfaction slowly crept over me.

"Can we sample what you make next week, Jane?" Tim asked as we got off the bus.

"Ever tried eating cottage pie with your fingers?" I giggled, suddenly feeling on top of the world, and glad after all that I was the only girl at our bus stop.

"There's always a first time," Tim replied promptly as we walked down the road. "There's nothing like home cooking."

Well, Mum and Miss Woodward would second that, I thought in amusement.

"I'd better bring you a knife and fork, Tim," I promised.

And, to my amazement, I found that I was actually looking forward to the following Wednesday.

THE END

The WARNING

PRUDENCE WELLS was going home for the school holidays at the end of summer term, 1911. It wasn't far, but it was a very slow train, stopping at every little station on the way. At one . . .

That man is staring at me!

As the train pulled away—

He seems to have disappeared. Such cheek! He *was* rather handsome, though!

At the next station—

It looks like the same man—but it can't be! How could he have reached here before the train?

I must be mistaken—but the two men did look very much alike.

As the train approached the third station, Prudence found herself looking out for the strange man.

No sign of him . . . but of course, there couldn't be! Even a motor car couldn't outrun the train!

But Prudence was wrong!

Help me . . . help . . . me . . .

But . . . but . . .

Next stop was Prudence's home, and she left the train feeling rather shaken.

You all right, miss? You look a bit pale.

Yes . . . yes, thank you.

Help? I wonder what he meant?

Then—

It's the mystery man . . . here! But how? I shan't rest until I find out what's going on! I must speak to him!

Excuse me, sir!

May I be of service, Miss?

114

THE END

115

Flying GEMS

The brightly — coloured, tiny hummingbirds of North and South America are indeed jewels of the bird family. Here are a few fascinating facts about them.

Hummingbirds were given their name by the first English colonists to North America, who noted that the Rubythroat's wings made a humming sound— yet many species are completely silent in flight.

Ruby-throat

Bee

Giant

There are over 300 varieties, ranging from the tiny Bee Hummingbird of Cuba, 63 mm. from bill to tail, to the Giant of Western South America, which measures a " huge " 215 mm.

56lbs 56

A hummingbird eats half its weight of sugar dai To gain an equivalent amount of energy, a m would have to eat 370 lb. of potatoes every day

Hummingbirds are very fond of water. This Brown Inca enjoys a bath from a garden sprinkler.

During the 19th Century, hummingbird feathe were imported to Europe as adornments for ladie hats. In one year, over 400,000 were sent from t West Indies alone.

Hummingbirds live on insects, and nectar from flowers. They have specially adapted bills to help them penetrate to the heart of a bloom. Here are two examples:- the Sicklebill (left) and the Swordbill.

Great courage is displayed by hummingbirds in defending their nests. These Velvet-Purple Coronets attack a giant Hawk Eagle.

Tails come in all shapes and sizes. Here is a Wire-crested Thorntail (top) and a very rare Marvellous Spatuletail.

Some idea of the size of hummingbirds can be gained from this picture of a Broad-tailed female feeding her young—with a 50p piece drawn to the same scale.

Have you ever thought about hair-dressing as a career? "Judy's" roving cameraman went along to a "Cut and Curl Studio" to find out how a trainee hairdresser spends her day.

The Cut 'n'

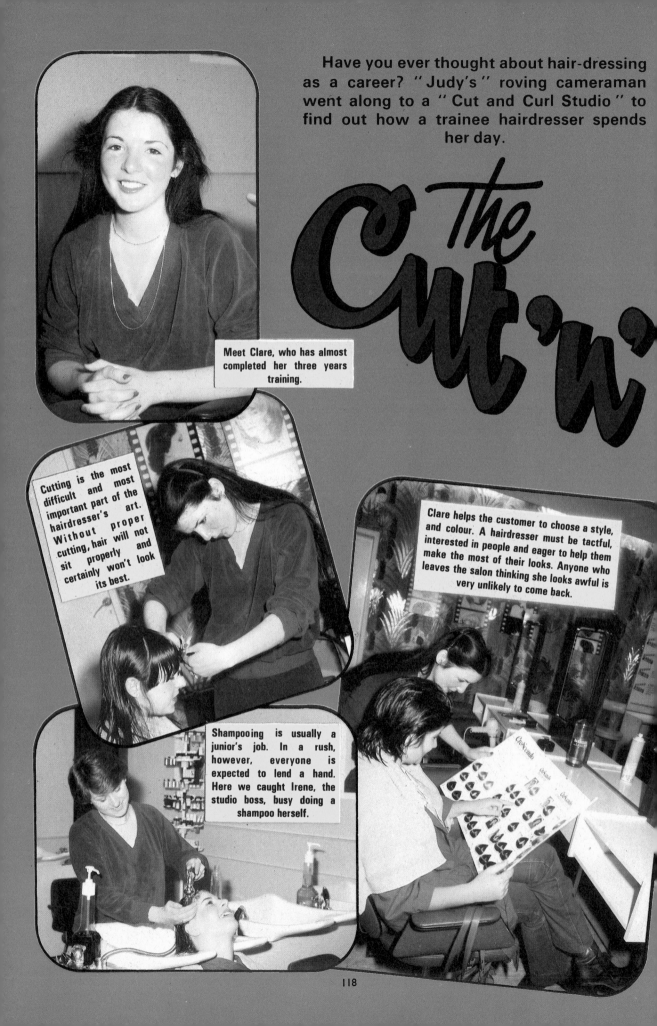

Meet Clare, who has almost completed her three years training.

Cutting is the most difficult and most important part of the hairdresser's art. Without proper cutting, hair will not sit properly and certainly won't look its best.

Clare helps the customer to choose a style, and colour. A hairdresser must be tactful, interested in people and eager to help them make the most of their looks. Anyone who leaves the salon thinking she looks awful is very unlikely to come back.

Shampooing is usually a junior's job. In a rush, however, everyone is expected to lend a hand. Here we caught Irene, the studio boss, busy doing a shampoo herself.

This time it is a shampoo and set. Any old roller won't do. They have to be the right size to get the required effect.

You must never forget details if you're a hairdresser. Hairdryers must always be set to suit your customer. You can't afford to leave someone hunched up in a chair for half-an-hour or more because you've left the dryer too low.

Curl Caper

next customer ...nts a tint. There is ...arge selection and ...is important to get ...e shade correct.

This strange device is called the octopus—what else? The gentle infra-red heat from the octopus makes a conditioning treatment work better.

Another satisfied customer is ready to leave the salon.

Party Girl

SAMANTHA PARRY'S only interest in life was going to parties—especially after she met Dominic.

It's after eleven, Dominic . . . I'll have to go home. My grandmother's ill.

Hey, Samantha, the party's only just beginning to liven up!

121

Dominic will be dancing with every girl there! Hello! What's the doctor doing here?

DOCTOR ON CALL

So you're back at last? Your grandmother's had a bad fall! Fortunately she managed to alert a passer-by, but you should have been here!

Says who?

Grandmother makes my life a misery! For two pins I'd put some of that stuff in her cocoa!

ZAP
FOR USE AS A DISINFECTANT ONLY
POISON

But if I did and was found out, I'd never inherit this house and all her money!

I'll be back in two days. Stay with her and ring me at once if she gets any worse.

What a bore of a week-end this is going to be!

The following afternoon—

I would so like a cup of tea, Samantha dear.

Well, it'll have to wait! I'm in the middle of watching a film! I'll bring it up later!

One of Samantha's school-friends rang.

Samantha? We're have a surprise party at my place tonight . . . come over!

A party? Just my luck! I'm stuck here with the old woman!

Pity . . . Dominic's coming!

Dominic? I'll be there!

122

Grandmother's asleep, anyway. I'm not sitting around here listening to her snoring!

This outfit should get me noticed by Dominic.

And it did.

Samantha, you're a knock-out!

Thanks, Dominic.

Girls, none of us will have a look-in with Dominic this evening!

The evening passed in a flash for Samantha.

Come on, you two! It's after midnight! Mum and Dad are due back. Party's over!

I hadn't noticed the time! I don't want to go back to look after boring old Granny just yet!

There's an all-night party at a friend's flat. We could go on there.

Great . . . let's go!

Dominic's powerful motor-cycle sped through the silent town.

I've never been to this part of town before.

That's the way life should be—one long party!

123

This is the place! They have a ball here!

You mingle, Samantha, while I go to find the host. I'd like you to meet him.

Don't be long!

These people seem strange and unhappy . . . and I don't think much of their choice of music!

The atmosphere didn't feel right to Samantha.

Ugh! The cola's warm and flat, and the sandwiches taste like they were made last year! I'm getting out of here!

Which way did we come in? I can't even remember coming in! I'll try that door.

124

Inside a tulip

Guildford Guildhall

Autumn leaves